First published in Great Britain 2022 by Farshore
An imprint of HarperCollins*Publishers*,
1 London Bridge Street, London SE1 9GF
www.farshore.co.uk

HarperCollins*Publishers* 1st Floor, Watermarque Building, Ringsend Road Dublin 4, Ireland

Written by Laura Jackson

© 2022 Disney Enterprises, Inc.

ISBN 978 0 0085 5524 5
Printed in Romania
001
A CIP catalogue record for this title is available from the British Library.

Parental guidance is advised for all craft and colouring activities. Always ask an adult to help when using glue, paint and scissors. Wear protective clothing and cover surfaces to avoid staining.

Stay safe online. Farshore is not responsible for content hosted by third parties.

FSC
www.fsc.org

MIX
Paper | Supporting
responsible forestry
FSC™ C007454

This
Encanto Annual 2023
belongs to:

....

....

Contents

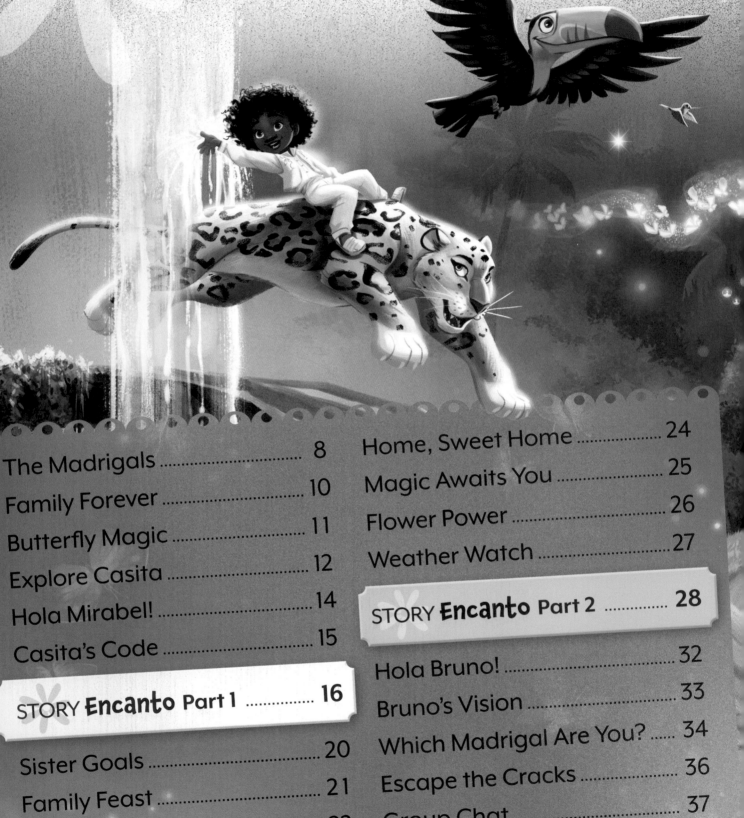

The Madrigals

The Madrigals are no ordinary family. Some of them have unique powers and they spread their magic all over the town of Encanto.

Fifteen-year-old Mirabel Madrigal wants to show you her family tree. Let's learn all about her extraordinary family and their special gifts.

Abuela Alma
As leader of the family, Abuela first brought magic to the family many years ago.

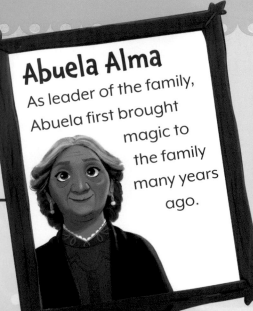

Pepa
Fun and a little wild, Pepa entertains the whole family. Her gift is to control the weather with her moods.

Félix
Félix doesn't have a gift, but he is the life of every party in the Encanto!

Julieta
Mother to Mirabel, Luisa and Isabela. Her gift is to heal people through food.

Agustín
Mirabel's father doesn't have a magical gift, but he always **sees** the bright side of life.

Bruno
The Madrigals don't talk about Bruno. His gift is to see into the future.

Camilo

A gifted storyteller, Camilo is never afraid to tell the truth. His gift is to shapeshift.

Dolores

Secrets are hard to keep when Dolores is around. Her gift is superhuman hearing.

Antonio

Mirabel's favourite little cousin is kind and gentle. His gift is to communicate with animals.

Luisa

Luisa helps everybody in the Encanto. Her magical gift is super-strength.

Isabela

Beautiful Isabela gets a lot of attention. Her gift is to make flowers bloom.

Say in Spanish

family	**familia**	*say fam-EE-lee-ah*
grandma	**abuela**	*say ah-BWEH-lah*
father	**padre**	*say PAH-dray*
mother	**madre**	*say MAH-dray*

Mirabel

Mirabel doesn't have a magical gift but she loves to make special things for her family.

Family Forever

Family is everything to the Madrigals. Now it's time to meet the people who make your life magical.

Draw pictures and write down the names of special people in your world.

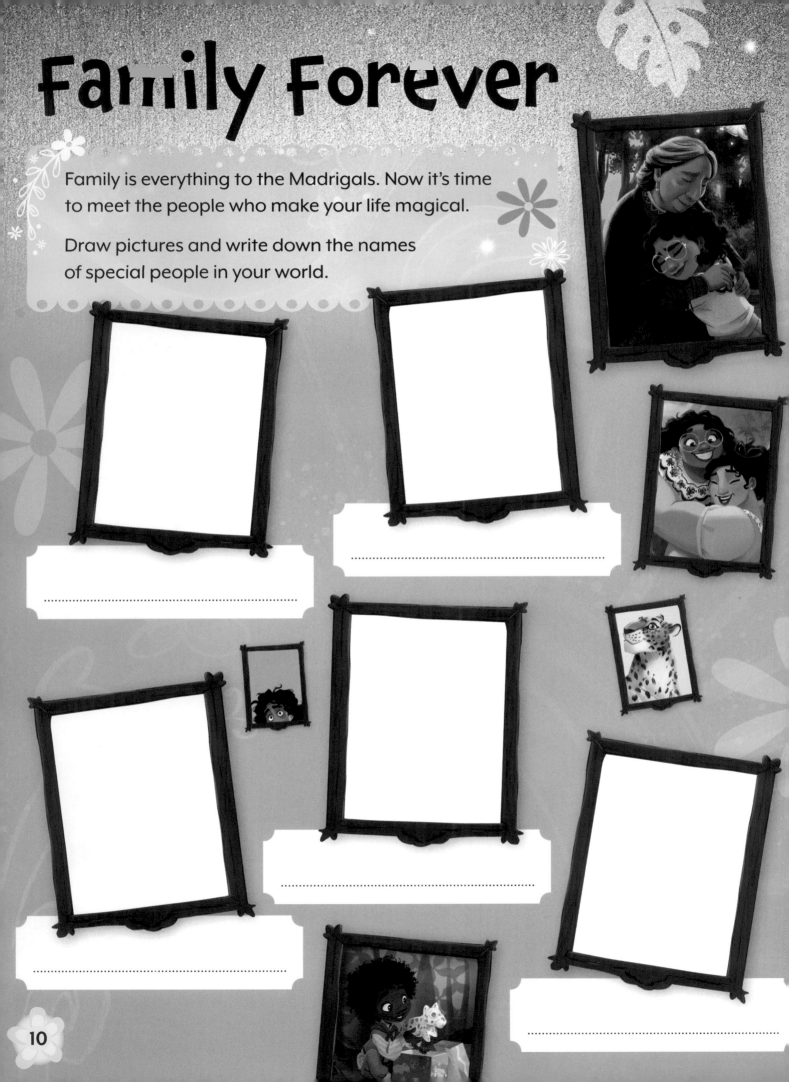

Butterfly Magic

Mirabel loves butterflies, and butterflies love her! Doodle lots more butterflies on the page and then colour in your fluttery picture.

Say in Spanish

butterfly **mariposa** *say mah-ree-POH-sah*

11

Explore Casita

Casita is not just a house. It's part of the Madrigal family. From magical doors to hidden worlds, there is fun and magic wherever you go.

Play the game and journey through Casita with Mirabel.

How to Play
* Each player places their counter on the START.
* The youngest player rolls the dice first and moves forward the number of spaces to match the number rolled.
* Each player then takes turns to roll the dice.
* Do Casita's challenges along the way.
* The first player to the FINISH is the winner!

START

1

2

3

4

Stop to see the flowers in Isabela's room.
Miss a go.

5

6

7

8

9

10

11

Race through Antonio's room.
Go forward 2 spaces.

12

13

14

29 Woah! A moving staircase takes you **back to 24.**

30

FINISH

28

27

24

23 You get stuck in sand in Casita's tower. **Go back 2 spaces.**

26 Some rats show you a shortcut. **Go forward 2 spaces.**

25

22

21

20

15

16

17 Whoosh! Follow Pepa's rainbow shortcut across Casita.

18

19

13

Hola Mirabel!

Mirabel works hard to help the people living in the Encanto. Being one of the few Madrigals without a special power can be tough. But Mirabel is brave and determined and she will find her own unique way to protect her family when everything falls apart ...

Mirabel is ...
creative, kind and loyal.

Mirabel loves ...
making her own clothes.

Mirabel's secret ...
she doesn't always feel so special in her family of heroes.

Make my family proud.

Say in Spanish

| hello | **hola** | *say OH-lah* |

Casita's Code

Mirabel has an important message for her family, but nobody is listening. Crack Casita's code to share what Mirabel has to say.

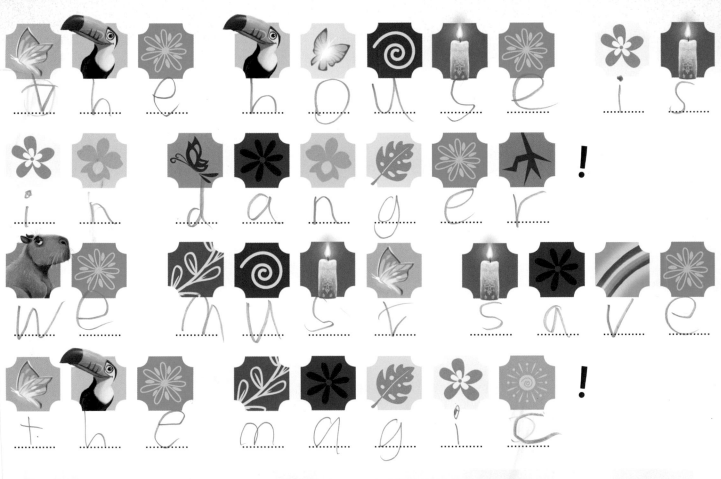

The house is
in danger!
we must save
the magic!

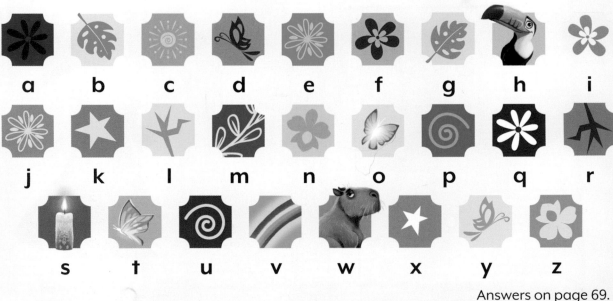

a b c d e f g h i
j k l m n o p q r
s t u v w x y z

Answers on page 69.

DISNEY ENCANTO

Tucked away in the mountains of Colombia, was a special town called Encanto. It was home to the Madrigals, an extraordinary family.

Abuela Alma was the head of the family. She brought magic here many years ago, when a candle had glowed brightly and a house called Casita grew around her.

Casita and the magic candle had protected Abuela's family ever since ...

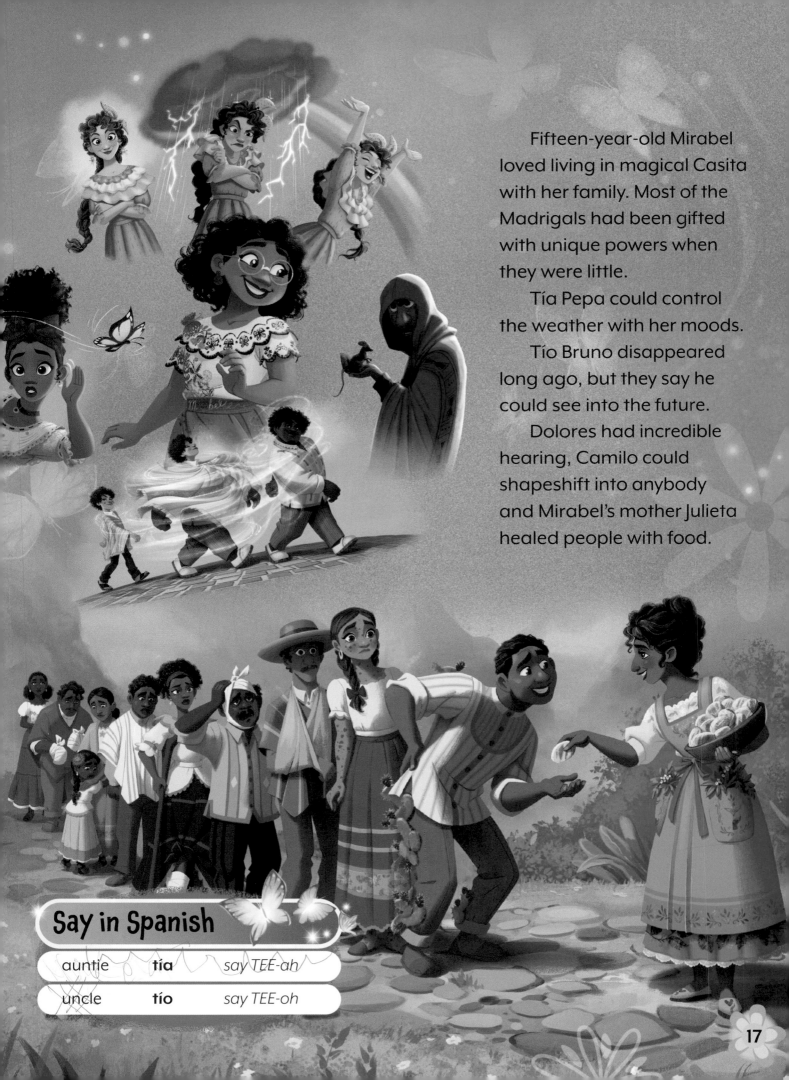

Fifteen-year-old Mirabel loved living in magical Casita with her family. Most of the Madrigals had been gifted with unique powers when they were little.

Tía Pepa could control the weather with her moods.

Tío Bruno disappeared long ago, but they say he could see into the future.

Dolores had incredible hearing, Camilo could shapeshift into anybody and Mirabel's mother Julieta healed people with food.

Say in Spanish

| auntie | **tía** | *say TEE-ah* |
| uncle | **tío** | *say TEE-oh* |

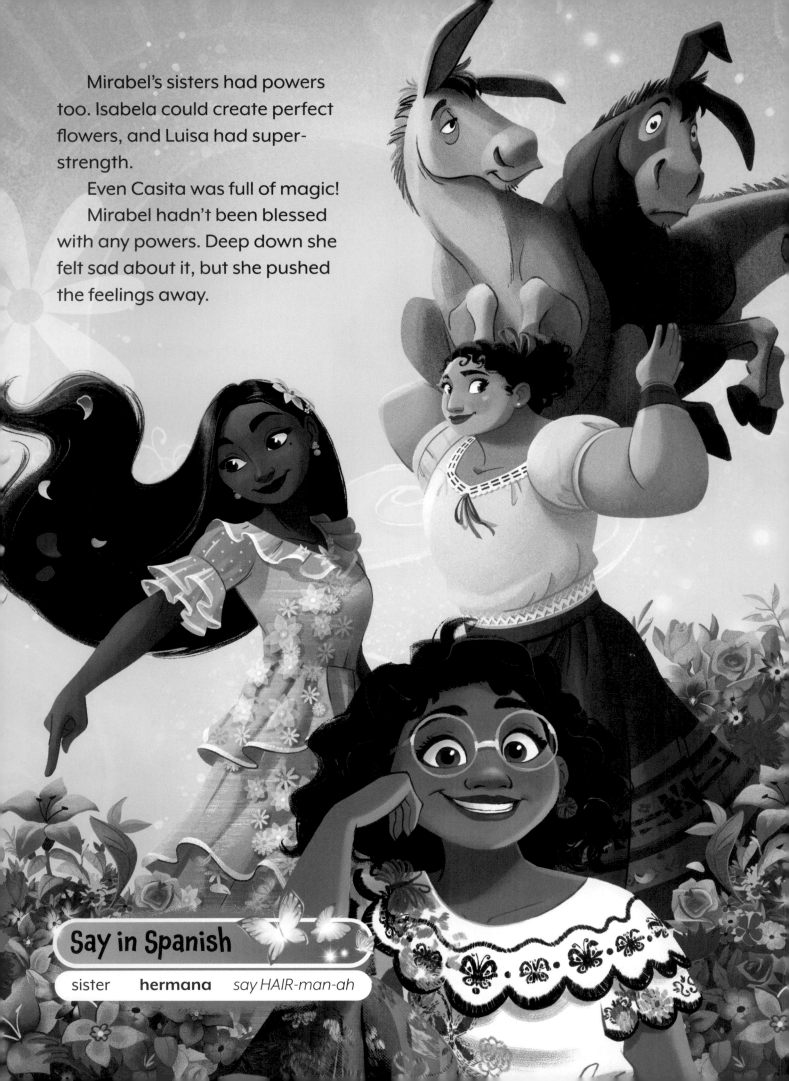

Mirabel's sisters had powers too. Isabela could create perfect flowers, and Luisa had super-strength.

Even Casita was full of magic! Mirabel hadn't been blessed with any powers. Deep down she felt sad about it, but she pushed the feelings away.

Say in Spanish

| sister | **hermana** | *say HAIR-man-ah* |

Mirabel moved around the house, deep in thought. Suddenly, she heard a CRACK! A tile fell from the roof and smashed.

"Casita ...?" Mirabel whispered.

Cracks appeared and the magic candle dimmed. Something wasn't right. Casita was in trouble ...

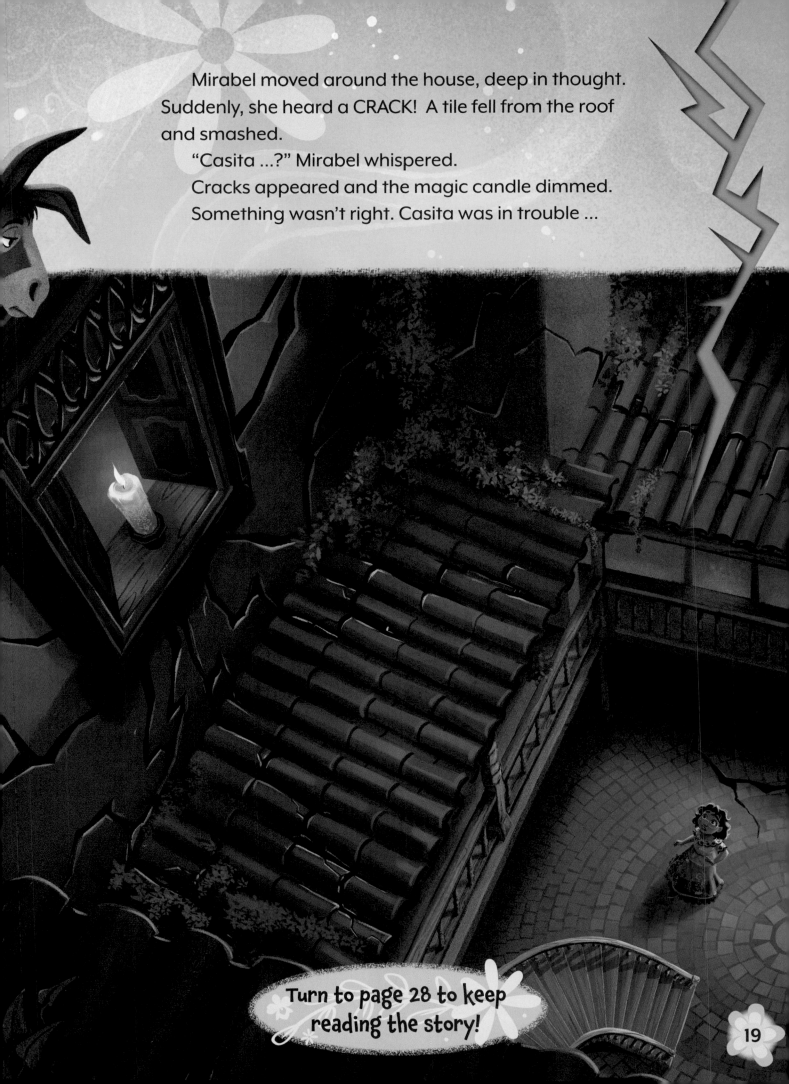

Turn to page 28 to keep reading the story!

Sister Goals

Isabela, Mirabel and Luisa all have very different gifts and personalities. Their differences are what makes the sisters stronger together! These pictures look the same, but there are five differences in picture 2. Can you spot them all?

1

2

20

Answers on page 69.

Family Feast

Dinner time around the Madrigal table is always fun, loud and magical. Design a new dinner plate, just for your family. Doodle things you all love around the edge and then draw your best family meal in the middle. Yum!

Hola Isabela!

Everything in Isabela's life looks perfect. From her long, flowing hair to her pretty flowers, Isabela is the golden child of the family. But deep down inside she has worries. Maybe being perfect isn't so perfect after all ...

Isabela is ...
graceful and beautiful and pretty perfect!

Isabela loves ...
making flowers bloom all over the Encanto.

Isabela's secret ...
she sometimes feels trapped in her family role.

Did somebody say **flowers?**

Say in Spanish

| flowers | **flores** | *say FLOR-rehs* |

Hidden Truths

Isabela likes to make her family happy, but there is something she is hiding from them. Follow each flower trail to discover a letter. Then write each letter in a space to find Isabela's secret.

Isabela doesn't want to get ...

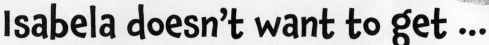

m a r r i e d

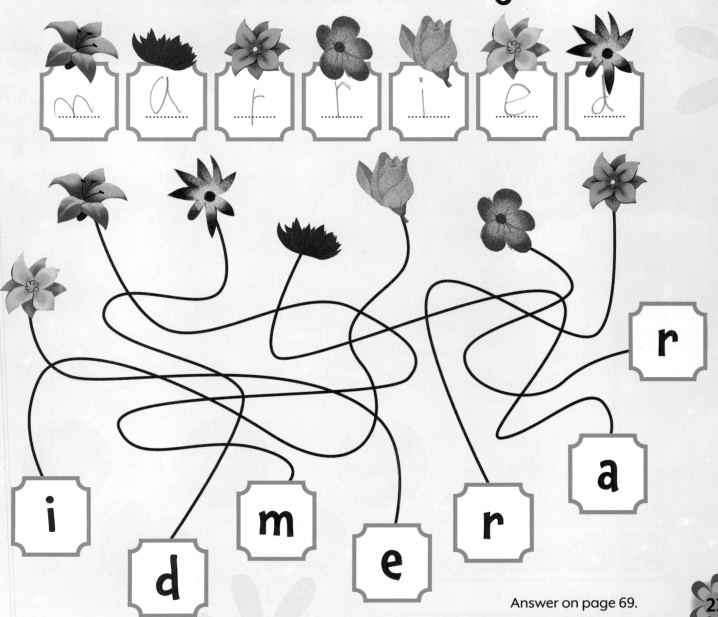

r

a

r

i m e

d

Answer on page 69.

Home, Sweet Home

Mirabel loves living **in** Casita with her big, noisy, extraordinary family. The Madrigal's magic is everywhere!

Can you spot the small close-ups in the big picture?

a

b

c

d

e

Say in Spanish

| home | casa | say KAH-sah |

Answers on page 69.

Magic Awaits You

Imagine you are in the Madrigal family, and it is your turn to open a magic door. What precious gift is waiting for you? Decorate the door to match your new gift. Make it unique to you.

Flower Power

It's party time in the Encanto, but Isabela hasn't finished decorating the town with flowers. Grab as many crayons as you can, set a timer for two minutes and colour in the flowers before the guests arrive!

Say in Spanish

| party | **fiesta** | *say Fee-ESS-tah* |

Weather Watch

Pepa can control the weather with her feelings. When she feels happy, the Encanto fills with sunshine. When she feels cross ... watch out for storms!

Draw lines to match up Pepa's moods to the different weather types.

1 happy

2 sad

3 angry

4 bored

5 excited

a

b

c

d

e

Say in Spanish

weather **clima** *say KLEE-mah*

Answers on page 69.

27

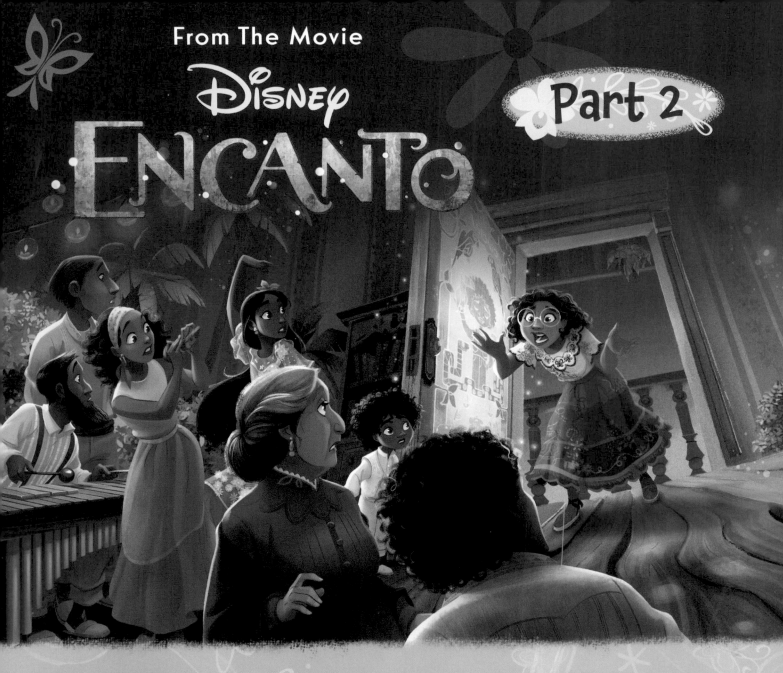

From The Movie

DISNEY
ENCANTO

Part 2

Mirabel raced off to get help, but when she arrived back all the cracks had disappeared.

"There is nothing wrong with La Casa Madrigal!" snapped Abuela. Abuela liked things to be perfect. She was cross at Mirabel.

Abuela might not believe her, but Mirabel knew Casita was in danger. And she was going to save the magic herself ...

The next day, Luisa admitted to Mirabel that something didn't feel quite right. Her own strength was fading.

"Before Tío Bruno left, he had some terrible vision," said Luisa. "If something is wrong, start with Bruno's tower. Find the vision!"

Bruno's tower was dark and creepy, but Mirabel climbed the hundreds of stairs to the top. If Bruno's vision was here, Mirabel was determined to find it.

Say in Spanish

danger **peligro** *say peh-LEE-groh*

29

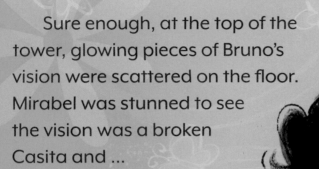

Sure enough, at the top of the tower, glowing pieces of Bruno's vision were scattered on the floor. Mirabel was stunned to see the vision was a broken Casita and ...

"Me ...?" gasped Mirabel.

Back in her room, Mirabel needed to find out more. She asked Tia Pepa about Bruno.

"We don't talk about Bruno!" warned Tia Pepa.

Pepa's husband, Félix, explained that bad things happened when Bruno looked into the future.

That night, Isabela was having a special party.
She was about to get engaged to be married.

Abuela wanted everything to be perfect, but
Mirabel's secret soon spread around the table.

"Mirabel's found Bruno's vision!" Dolores blurted out.

Chaos took over. Huge cracks shot across the floor
and everyone's powers fizzed out of control.

Something even stranger was happening down on the
ground. Rats were scurrying away – with Bruno's vision!

Turn to page 44 to keep
reading the story!

31

Hola Bruno!

Bruno has the amazing gift of premonition. For many years, he helped people in the Encanto see into their future. But when his family started to think Bruno's visions were making bad things happen, he disappeared. Nobody is allowed to talk about Bruno, until Mirabel unlocks the past ...

Bruno is ...
mysterious, gentle and lonely.

Bruno loves ...
his family and his loyal rats!

Bruno's secret ...
he had a vision that Mirabel was connected to the magic disappearing.

My gift wasn't helping the family ...

Say in Spanish

| rat | **rata** | *say RRAH-tah* |

32

Bruno's Vision

Bruno is worried his visions will get his family into trouble, but Mirabel just wants to know the truth. Put the jumbled picture into the right order so Bruno can use his gift again.

1

2

3

4

5

6

Answers on page 69.

Which Madrigal Are you?

The Madrigals are all proud to be different and to have their own unique personalities. Take the quiz to find out which Madrigal you are most like.

1 What would be your perfect day?

a   Trying out a new sport

b   Making your own outfit for a party

c   Planting flowers

d   Hanging out with cute animals

2 What word best describes you?

a   Tough

b   Funny

c   Nurturing

d   Kind

3 What would be your perfect gift?

a   Sports equipment

b   Embroidery set

c   House plant

d   Book about animals

4 What would you do to cheer up a friend?

a   Take them for a run outdoors

b   Make them a card

c   Send them some flowers

d   Give them a hug

5 How would you describe your style?

a   Comfortable

b   Fun and colourful

c   Pretty and elegant

d   You don't really care what you wear!

6 You are happiest when ...

a   You are helping others

b   Your family are happy

c   You are out in nature

d   You are with animals

7 Your dream job would be ...

a An athlete

b A clothes designer

c A gardener

d A vet

8 8. What is your favourite thing about nature?

a Fresh air

b Butterflies

c Flowers and plants

d Animals

9 How do you like to help people in your family?

a Tidy up

b Create something to make them happy

c Make your home look pretty

d Say kind words to show you care

Mostly **a**s
You are Luisa

You are strong, active and work hard to help your family. Sometimes you can work a bit too hard. You need to remember to chill, too! A star in all sports, your energy fills the world.

Mostly **b**s
You are Mirabel

You are a bright spark bursting with fun and positive vibes. Your creative skills impress everyone you know. From making crafts to prepping parties, you spread creativity wherever you go.

Mostly **c**s
You are Isabela

When you are surrounded by nature, you are at your happiest. You have a golden touch with making everything look beautiful. And when anyone around you is sad, you show them the magic of nature!

Mostly **d**s
You are Antonio

Animals love you and you love them! You also love to hang out with your family, too. Your kind words and sweet thoughts make the people (and animals!) around you feel happy.

Escape the Cracks

Casita is cracking! Guide Mirabel through the house, following the butterflies to safety.

Only follow the butterflies in this order:

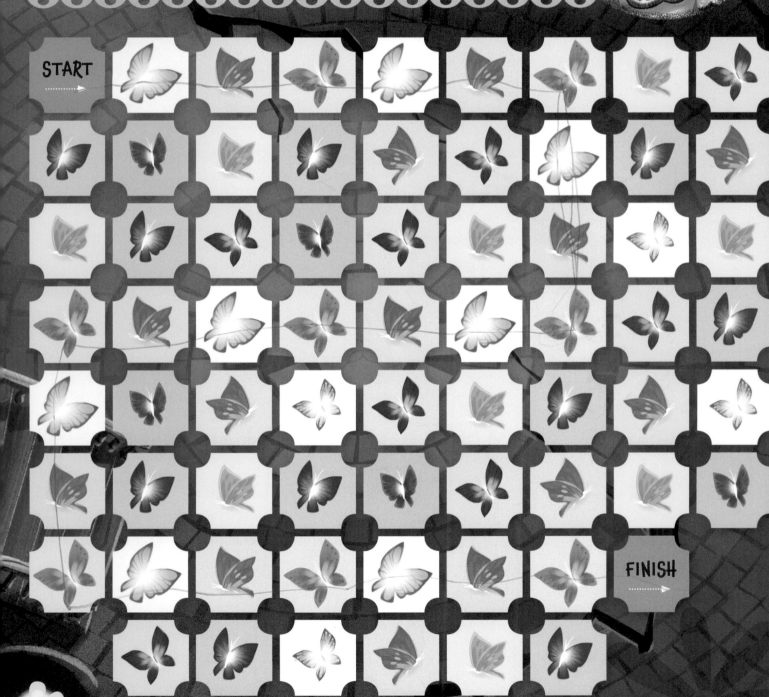

Answers on page 69.

Group Chat

What do you think Antonio and his animal friends are talking about today? Use the dots as a colour guide to shade in the picture.

Write what Antonio and the animals are saying.

Say in Spanish

talk   **hablar**   *say ah-BLAHR*

37

Hola Abuela Alma!

Abuela is the leader of the family. Her love for her husband created the miracle of Casita many years ago. Abuela has spent her whole life protecting this magic for her family. Her fiery protection can sometimes push her family away, but her love is strong and family is everything to Abuela.

Abuela is ...
determined, tough and brave.

Abuela loves ...
her family, the magic of the Encanto and to always be right!

Abuela's secret ...
she regrets her need for everything to be perfect.

Say in Spanish

miracle   **milagro**   *say mee-LAH-groh*

This candle blessed us with a **miracle**.

38

A Helping Hand

Abuela loves her family fiercely, even if she doesn't always get it right. Today she is trying to show her family just how much she cares. Play her kindness wheel to help your family, too.

How to Play

* Throw a dice to get a number 1 – 6.
* Now do the matching challenge.
* Repeat every day until you have done all six challenges.

2 Help to tidy up at home.

3 Help to set the table for dinner.

1 Make a surprise gift for somebody.

4 Make a picture for somebody.

6 Give somebody a big hug!

5 Tell somebody they are perfect as they are.

Say in Spanish

help **ayudar** *say ah-yoo-DAHR*

39

Perfect As You Are

Mirabel sometimes feels sad that she doesn't have a magical gift, like the rest of her family. Guide Julieta and Antonio to Mirabel so they can tell her she is perfect just the way she is.

Say in Spanish

perfect   **perfecto**   *say pehr-FEHK-toh*

Answers on page 69.

Say What?

Dolores can hear EVERYTHING that everyone says. Her superpowered hearing means it can be hard to keep secrets in Casita.

Draw lines to match the speech to the person.

1
"The rats told me you don't wash your underwear."

2
"I will save the magic for my family."

3
"I don't do visions anymore!"

4
"You're gonna make me drop the donkeys!"

5
"We are fine. The magic is strong!"

a

b

c

d

e

Answers on page 69.

Animal Antics

Antonio loves his new rainforest room and best of all, his new animal friends. Take a close look at the pictures below. Circle the odd one out in each row.

1

2

3

4

Answers on page 69.

W_ Don't Talk About Bruno

Bruno is hiding from his family in a dark, secret tower. Help Mirabel find the path to her uncle before he escapes again.

Answers on page 69.

Mirabel followed the rats down a dark passageway. A flash of lightning ahead revealed a shadow ... Tio Bruno!

"You ... never left," gasped Mirabel.

He told Mirabel all about his vision many years ago, but he didn't know what it meant.

With a lot of persuasion, Bruno agreed to use his gift once more. This time a vision of Isabela hugging Mirabel floated into the air.

Mirabel was annoyed that it was Isabela who had to help.

All her life, Mirabel had lived in the shadow of her perfect sister.

"The fate of the family is not up to her," said Bruno. "It's up to you."

Mirabel knew she had to apologise for ruining Isabela's party.

At first, Isabela refused to hug, or even talk, to her sister!

Say in Spanish

| hug | **abrazo** | *say ah-BRAH-soh* |

Then to Mirabel's surprise, Isabela began to share some secrets of her own. When she told Mirabel she was only getting married to please her family, something amazing happened.

Instead of making perfect flowers, unique and prickly plants popped into life. The more Isabela shared her true feelings, the more messy fun the sisters had together.

Isabela felt free from being perfect for the first time in her life.

Say in Spanish

secret	secreto	say seh-KREH-toh

Not everybody in Casita was happy about Isabela's new, messy ways.

"What have you done?" Abuela shouted.

Mirabel explained that Isabela wasn't happy being perfect.

"Bruno left because of you," Abuela shouted at Mirabel. "Isabela's out of control because of you!"

A tremor shook the Encanto.

"We'll never be good enough!" said Mirabel. "No matter how hard any of us tries. The miracle is dying because of you!"

Turn to page 56 to keep reading the story!

Shapeshifting

Camilo loves to surprise his family with a quick shapeshift. Read the clues to work out who he has transformed into today.

Clue 1:
☐ I am wearing a dress.

Clue 2:
☐ I am not super strong.

Clue 3:
☐ I am not wearing an apron.

Clue 4:
☐ I am in a happy mood.

Camilo has transformed into ....

Answers on page 69.

Madrigal Door Hanger

© Disney

Make and decorate your own Casita hanger for your bedroom door.

How to Make:

* Ask an adult to cut out your door hanger.
* Use crayons to colour in the design.
* Now hang it on your door when you want your family to come in or to stay out!

Come in!

KEEP OUT!

Family Forever!

© Disney

Party Prep

Castita is perfect for parties. Why not throw a mini party in your own home? Follow the instructions to create some magical party bunting.

How to Make:

* Ask an adult to cut out the bunting.
* Colour in the bunting pieces.
* Measure out a length of string or ribbon.
* Use sticky tape to stick the string to the back of the bunting shapes.

© Disney

© Disney

© Disney

© Disney

© Disney

Now hang your party bunting up!

You can flip over your bunting flags and choose from two designs.

54

Burning Bright

When Mirabel was five, Abuela told her all about the **magic** of the candle. The burning candle keeps the magic of the Encanto strong.

Can you find these words from Abuela's story hiding in the grid?

t	n	s	t	r	o	n	g
u	a	n	b	k	u	i	f
t	o	q	o	u	h	r	a
n	m	d	s	k	r	h	m
c	a	n	d	l	e	n	i
i	g	w	b	o	o	z	l
g	i	f	t	o	o	v	y
r	c	v	e	l	l	a	e

magic
candle
burn
love
strong
family
gift

Say in Spanish

candle   **vela**   *say BEH-lah*

Answers on page 69.

55

DISNEY ENCANTO

Part 4

A huge crack snaked up through Casita. The magic candle fell out of the window.

In a flash, everything changed. The family's gifts began to fade, Casita crumbled and the candle went out.

The miracle of Casita was broken.

Heartbroken, Mirabel ran and ran and ran. When she came to a stop by a river, Mirabel felt all alone. Until somebody slowly sat down beside her ... Abuela.

"I'm sorry!" Mirabel said through tears.

"We are broken because of me," said Abuela.

Abuela confessed she was so afraid of losing the magic, that she demanded too much from her family.

As Abuela wrapped her arms tightly around Mirabel, glowing butterflies swirled and Bruno arrived on a horse! To his big surprise, Abuela hugged him too.

Say in Spanish

afraid   **temer**   *say teh-MEHR*

57

Meanwhile, a darkness had covered the Encanto. No one spoke, certain that all was lost.

Suddenly, Mirabel, Abuela and Bruno appeared in a glow of butterflies. Everybody gasped when they saw Bruno!

Abuela said sorry to her family. Sorry for expecting too much.

"It's going to be OK," said Mirabel. She told her family that the real miracle wasn't their magic or their gifts … it was simply all of them.

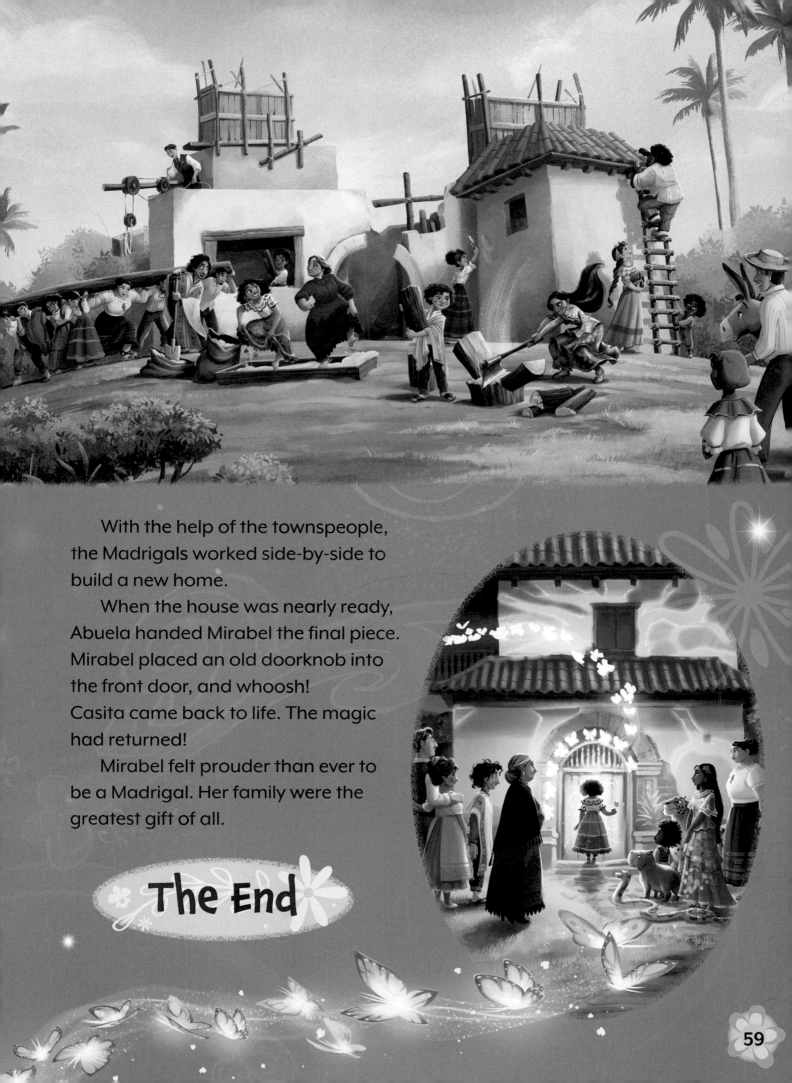

With the help of the townspeople, the Madrigals worked side-by-side to build a new home.

When the house was nearly ready, Abuela handed Mirabel the final piece. Mirabel placed an old doorknob into the front door, and whoosh! Casita came back to life. The magic had returned!

Mirabel felt prouder than ever to be a Madrigal. Her family were the greatest gift of all.

The End

Better Together

Casita has crumbled to the ground and the magic candle has burned out! Can you help the Madrigals come together to rebuild their Encanto?

Guide Mirabel through their broken home, picking up her family along the way.

When everybody reaches the finish, colour in the candle's flame. Now the magic of Casita can begin again!

START

FINISH

Hola Luisa!

Super strong and super helpful, Luisa spends most of her days pulling, pushing and carrying everything and anything for the townspeople. From piles of donkeys to giant wagons, nothing is too big, heavy or noisy for Luisa!

Luisa is ...
strong, tough and funny.

Luisa loves ...
lifting weights and helping people.

Luisa's secret ...
she hides big emotions under her tough personality.

The magic of family ...

Say in Spanish

| strong | **fuerte** | *say FWEHR-teh* |

Working Out

Luisa is on a mission to do some serious lifting today. Do the sums to work out how much she is carrying.

1  +  +  = 10

2  +  +  = 6

3  +  +  +  =  4

Say in Spanish

donkey   **burro**   *say BOO-rroh*

63

Answers on page 69.

Time to Rebuild

Stone by stone, the Madrigals build up a new Casita. Their magic has disappeared, but with some hard work (and a whole lot of help), the family can do anything!

Look at this picture for 20 seconds. Now cover it up and see how much you remember.

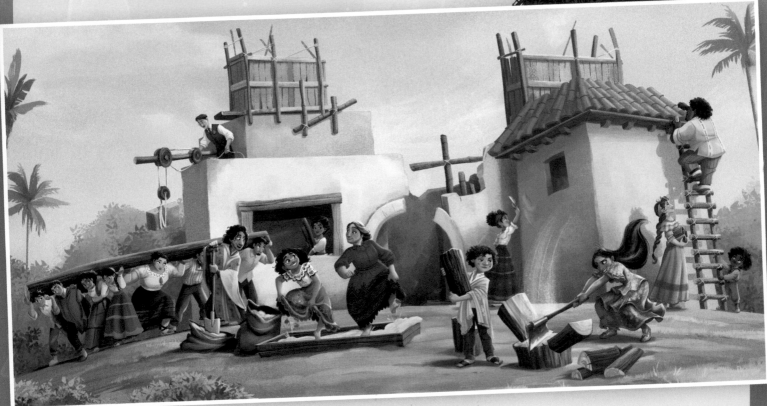

1. Who is stamping in the cement? ....

2. What colour is Bruno's robe? *green* ....

3. Is it sunny or rainy? *it is sunny* ....

4. Who is holding the ladder for Félix? ....

5. What is Bruno holding? ....

Say in Spanish

| work | **trabajo** | *say trah-BAH-hoh* |

Answers on page 69.

Perfectly Imperfect

Mirabel has shown Isabela that being imperfect is the best way to be. Use as many crazy colour patterns as you can to shade in Isabela's dress. She wants to look messy and fun!

Doodle lots of silly shaped plants and flowers too.

Casita Designs

66

Mirabel's Gift

When Mirabel wasn't blessed with the miracle of a special power, she felt sad and lonely. But all along, Mirabel had the greatest gift of all.

Go back through the book and find the hidden words to reveal Mirabel's own special gift.

All the secret words will look like this:

word

Go back to page 14.

Secret word: ....

Go back to page 8.

Secret word: ....

Go back to page 62.

Secret word: ....

Go back to page 55.

Secret word: ....

Go back to page 24.

Secret word: ....

Go back to page 41.

Secret word: ....

Say in Spanish

gift	**regalo**	*say rreh-GAH-loh*

Answers on page 69.

Word List

Did you spot all the Spanish words? Tick each word when you say them.

☐ family — **familia** — *say fam-EE-lee-ah*

☐ grandma — **abuela** — *say ah-BWEH-lah*

☐ father — **padre** — *say PAH-dray*

☐ mother — **madre** — *say MAH-dray*

☐ butterfly — **mariposa** — *say mah-ree-POH-sah*

☐ hello — **hola** — *say OH-lah*

☐ auntie — **tía** — *say TEE-ah*

☐ uncle — **tío** — *say TEE-oh*

☐ sister — **hermana** — *say HAIR-man-ah*

☐ flowers — **flores** — *say FLOR-rehs*

☐ home — **casa** — *say KAH-sah*

☐ party — **fiesta** — *say fee-ESS-tah*

☐ weather — **clima** — *say KLEE-mah*

☐ danger — **peligro** — *say peh-LEE-groh*

☐ rat — **rata** — *say RRAH-tah*

☐ talk — **hablar** — *say ah-BLAHR*

☐ miracle — **milagro** — *say mee-LAH-groh*

☐ help — **ayudar** — *say ah-yoo-DAHR*

☐ perfect — **perfecto** — *say pehr-FEHK-toh*

☐ hug — **abrazo** — *say ah-BRAH-soh*

☐ secret — **secreto** — *say seh-KREH-toh*

☐ candle — **vela** — *say BEH-lah*

☐ afraid — **temer** — *say teh-MEHR*

☐ strong — **fuerte** — *say FWEHR-teh*

☐ donkey — **burro** — *say BOO-rroh*

☐ work — **trabajo** — *say trah-BAH-hoh*

☐ gift — **regalo** — *say rreh-GAH-loh*

Answers

PAGE 15 Casita's Code
The house is in danger!
We must save the magic!

PAGE 20 Sister Goals

PAGE 23 Hidden Truths
Isabela doesn't want to get married.

PAGE 24 Home Sweet Home

PAGE 27 Weather Watch
1 - e, 2 - a, 3 - d, 4 - c, 5 - b.

PAGE 33 Bruno's Vision

5 4 2 6 3 1

PAGE 36 Escape the Cracks

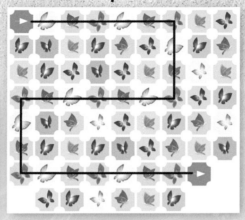

PAGE 40 Perfect as You Are

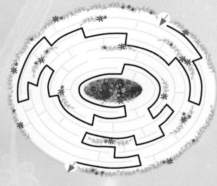

PAGE 41 Say What?
1 - b, 2 - c, 3 - d, 4 - e, 5 - a.

PAGE 42 Animal Antics

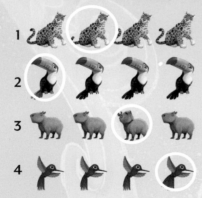

1
2
3
4

PAGE 43 We Don't Talk About Bruno
Path b leads to Bruno.

PAGE 48 Shapeshifting
Camilo has transformed into Mirabel.

PAGE 55 Burning Bright

t	n	s	t	r	o	n	g
u	a	n	b	k	u	i	f
t	o	q	o	u	h	r	a
n	m	d	s	k	r	m	m
c	a	n	d	l	e	n	i
i	g	w	b	o	o	z	l
g	i	f	t	o	o	v	y
r	c	v	e	l	l	a	e

PAGE 60-61 Better Together

PAGE 63 Working Out
1 - 10, 2 - 6, 3 - 4.

PAGE 64 Time to Rebuild
1. Mirabel and Abuela
2. green
3. sunny
4. Antonio
5. spade

PAGE 67 Mirabel's Gift
Mirabel sees the magic in everyone.